CHART HITS

Wise Publications
part of The Music Sales Group
London/New York/Paris/Sydney/Copenhagen/Berlin/Madrid/Hong Kong/Tokyo

24K Magic

Words & Music by Philip Lawrence, Peter Hernandez & Christopher "Brody" Brown

The first single of his third studio album of the same title, Mars calls this song 'an invitation to the party'. The fun, celebratory vibe of the track echoes his previous smash hit, 'Uptown Funk', which was storming the charts at No. 1 while '24K Magic' was in the making. The track affirms that Mars's party atmosphere is of the highest quality with the reference to 24-karat gold—the purest of them all!

Hints & Tips: For a funkier rhythm, try playing the dampened strums as written in the second box below.

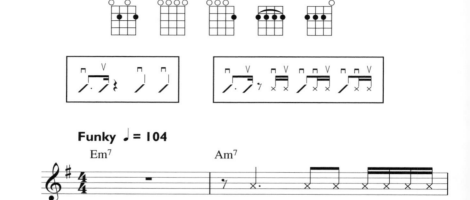

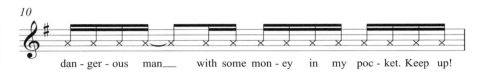

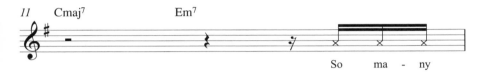

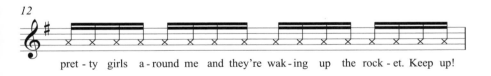

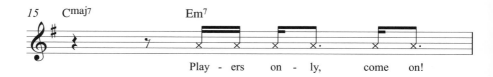

15 C^maj7 Em^7

Play - ers on - ly, come on!

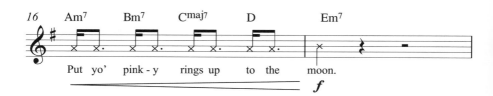

16 Am^7 Bm^7 C^maj7 D Em^7

Put yo' pink - y rings up to the moon.

f

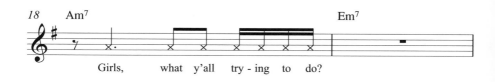

18 Am^7 Em^7

Girls, what y'all try - ing to do?

20 Am^7

Twen - ty - four ka - rat ma - gic in the

21 Em^7 Am^7 C^maj7

air.___ Head to toe,___ soul

23 Em^7

play - er. Look out!

Ain't My Fault

Words & Music by Uzoechi Emenike, Zara Larsson & Mack

After winning Talang, a Swedish talent show, at the age of 10, Zara Larsson was destined for a career in music. Still only in her late teens when the single was released, 'Ain't My Fault' describes Larsson's attraction to a good-looking man and her subsequent actions, for which she thinks she shouldn't be made responsible. Initially, it was written about two women arguing over a man, but Zara appealed to the 'girl code'—that girls should stick together—and decided not to record the original lyrics.

Hints & Tips: In the strumming pattern, beats 2, 3 and 4 can be emphasised with an accented strum (as written below).

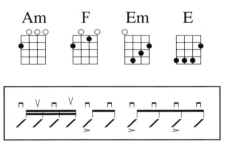

Strong ♩ = 130

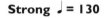

Bad Things

**Words & Music by Richard Baker, Madison Love, Anthony Scalzo, Karla Cabello,
Alex Schwartz & Joe Khajadourian**

'Bad Things' is a song about the relationship between a 'good girl' and a 'bad boy', played by Camila Cabello
of Fifth Harmony girl group fame, and rapper, Machine Gun Kelly. In order to record the track, the duo had
to collaborate long-distance over the phone and FaceTime. It took over 100 takes before the pair were finally
happy with Cabello's vocal line!

Hints & Tips: Keep a steady tempo with a slight emphasis on beats 2 and 4.

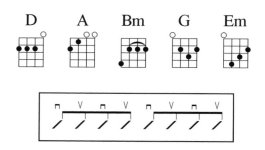

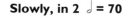

Slowly, in 2 ♩ = 70

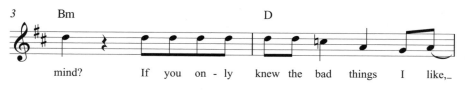

Am I out of my head? Am I out of my

mind? If you on - ly knew the bad things I like,_

__ don't think that I can ex - plain__ it.

7 Em / A

What can I say?_ It's com - pli - cat - ed._

9 D / A

Don't mat - ter what you_ say,_ don't mat - ter what you_ do._

11 Bm / D

_ I on - ly wan - na do bad things to you,_

13 G / D

_ so good that you can't ex - plain_ it.

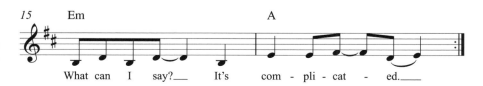

15 Em / A

What can I say?_ It's com - pli - cat - ed._

Castle On The Hill

Words & Music by Benjamin Levin & Ed Sheeran

Famous for his down-to-earth attitude to being a celebrity, Sheeran wrote this song about his home town of Framlingham in Suffolk, saying, 'This is a love song for Suffolk, because I don't think anyone has ever done that'. The video for the song was shot in Framlingham and even stars an Ed Sheeran lookalike, who is actually a young student at Thomas Mills High School, where Sheeran used to study!

Hints & Tips: Make sure you keep an even rhythm throughout and remember to observe the dynamic markings.

And tast - ed the sweet___ per - fume__ of the moun -

- tain___ grass I rolled down.

I was young - er then.

Take me back to when___ I

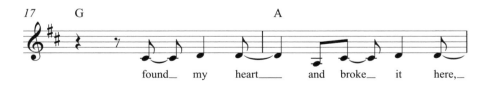

found_ my heart___ and broke_ it here,_

___ made friends_ and lost___ them through_ the years.

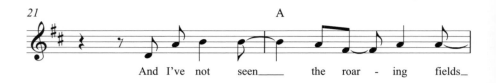

And I've not seen___ the roar - ing fields___

___ in so___ long, I___ know I've___ grown,

but I can't wait___ to go___ home.

I'm on___ my way,___

mf

driv - ing___ at nine - ty___ down

those coun - try lanes,___

sing - ing___ to 'Ti - ny Danc - er', and

I miss___ the way_____ you___ make

me___ feel, and it's___ real, when

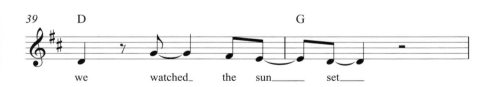

we watched_ the sun___ set___

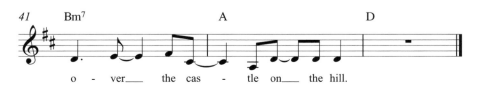

o - ver___ the cas - tle on___ the hill.

By Your Side

Words & Music by George Astasio, Jason Pebworth, Jonathan Shave, Guy Robin & Grace Barker

Jonas Blue's first single was a house music cover of Tracy Chapman's 'Fast Car', which shot him to fame in 2016. 'By Your Side' is another club classic and the third single from the electronic dance producer. Teenage singing sensation RAYE features on the track and has worked with a number of other contemporary names, including Charlie XCX and the songwriter/producer Jax Jones, whose song featuring RAYE also appears in this book.

Hints & Tips: For the verses, try playing the strumming pattern with an open feel, then in the chorus play it with a more dampened sound for variation.

tear it down,_ get - tin' lost____ in the sound_ of our hearts_

beat - in'.____ Take me here,_

take me now,_ get - tin' lost____ in the crowd_ with you._

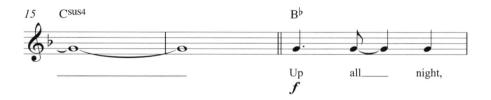

Up all____ night,

f

I wait - ed for you all my_____ life.

Hold my hand and keep me close, I'll nev - er let you

go, no, not____ to - night.____

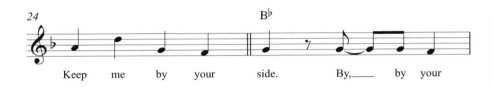

Keep me by your side. By,____ by your

side. By,____ by your side. By,____ by your

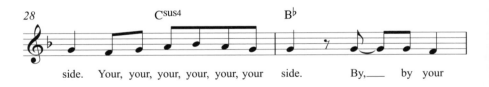

side. Your, your, your, your, your, your side. By,____ by your

side. By,____ by your side. By,____ by...

Keep me by your side.____

Closer

Words & Music by Joseph King, Isaac Slade, Shaun Frank,
Ashley Frangipane, Andrew Taggart & Frederic Kennett

Keeping it stateside, American DJ duo The Chainsmokers got together with American singer-songwriter Halsey to record 'Closer'. Listeners are treated to the first vocal performance from The Chainsmokers' Drew Taggart as he sings with Halsey in a romantic comedy-style duet. The duo cite pop-punk band Blink 182 as one of their biggest influences for the track, particularly their song 'I Miss You', which they played on repeat!

Hints & Tips: For variation, play the rhythm *staccato* until bars 17–25, where it can be more *legato*.

Relaxed ♩ = 96

Hey, I was do-ing just fine be-fore_ I met_ you, I drink too

mp

much and that's_ an is - sue but I'm o - kay.

Hey, you tell your friends it was nice to meet_ them but I

Human

Words & Music by Jamie Hartman & Rory Graham

Rag'n'Bone Man is deeply influenced by blues and hip-hop music, and this inspiration infiltrates into his own sound, as you can hear in 'Human'. His first taste of performing in public came when his father persuaded him to sing at a local blues jam at the age of 19, after which he was booked for local gigs and felt encouraged to work on his own projects. The stage name Rag'n'Bone Man was a result of his appreciation of *Steptoe & Son*, a British TV sitcom about a father and son's 'rag-and-bone' business.

Hints & Tips: This song uses the chord Bm, which might be a bit tricky for some beginners. Bm can also be played without the 4th string, which makes it easier (see the Bm* chord box below).

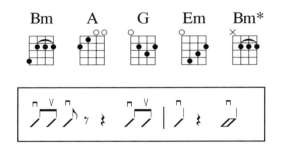

Sparse ♩ = 150

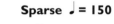

but I'm on - ly hu -

- man, af - ter all,_____ I'm on - ly hu -

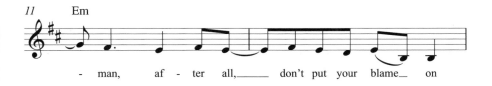

- man, af - ter all,_____ don't put your blame___ on

me, don't put your blame___ on me.

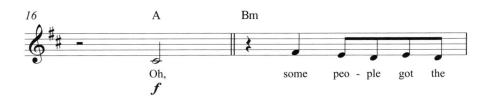

Oh, some peo - ple got the

real___ prob - lems,___ some peo - ple out of

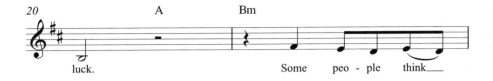

luck.   Some   peo - ple   think___

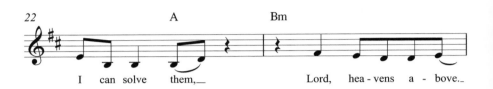

I   can solve   them,___   Lord,   hea - vens   a - bove.___

___   I'm   on - ly   hu -   man,   af - ter   all,___

___   I'm   on - ly   hu -   man,   af - ter   all,___

___   don't   put   the   blame___   on   me,

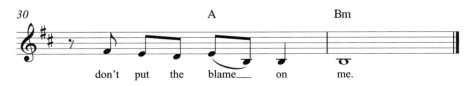

don't   put   the   blame___   on   me.

I Would Like

Words & Music by Zara Larsson, Oliver Peterhof, Marcus Lomax, Jordan Johnson, Alexander Izquierdo, Anthony Kelly, Karen Chin, James Abrahart & Stefan Johnson

Larsson brings back the 1990s in this adaptation of Sasha's 1998 tune 'Dat Sexy Body'. Sasha's original version harks back to her Jamaican roots, with elements of reggae and dancehall, while Larsson reinvents the song as a millennial club classic. In one performance of 'I Would Like', Larsson made headlines for an entirely different reason—a bizarre choice of stage outfit saw her wearing a bright pink, fluffy coat, leading the press to make comparisons with the British children's TV character Bagpuss!

Hints & Tips: This song features an off-beat strumming pattern (see below). Practise slowly at first to get the up-strokes in the right place.

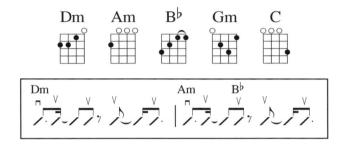

I did-n't know___ that I could want you so

deep, un-til I saw___ you with some-one who's not

me.___ You got me play - ing in a game that ain't

15 Gm · · · Bb · C

when it comes so nat - 'ral - ly?___ I would

17 Dm · · · Am · Bb

like to get to know you,___ ba - by,___

19 Dm · · · Am · Bb

like to get un-der your sex - y bo - dy. I would

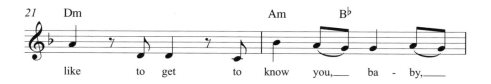

21 Dm · · · Am · Bb

like to get to know you,___ ba - by,___

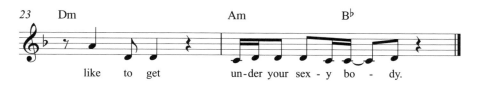

23 Dm · · · Am · Bb

like to get un-der your sex - y bo - dy.

Let Me Love You

Words & Music by Justin Bieber, William Grigahcine, Brian Lee, Steven Marsden, Andrew Wotman, Carl Rosen, Teddy Mendez & Edwin Perez
Arranged by Alex Tamposi, Louis Bell & Lumidee Cedeno

From his debut album, *Encore*, DJ Snake collaborated with young pop idol Justin Bieber for this track about a guy who refuses to give up on his relationship. The album cover art shows DJ Snake in the desert, walking towards a French metro station, which illustrates his dual heritage — his parents are from North Africa and he himself is Parisian. The DJ is well known for his dancefloor anthems, having had previous hits like 'Turn Down For What', featuring rapper Lil Jon.

Hints & Tips: This song uses the chord Bm, which might be a bit tricky for some beginners. Bm can also be played without the 4th string, which makes it easier (see the Bm* chord box below).

mir - rors keep us wait - ing on a mi - ra - cle, on a

mi - ra - cle. Say, go through the dark - est of days,

hea - ven's a heart - break a - way.

Nev-er let you go, nev-er let me down. Oh,

it's been a hell of a ride, driv - ing the edge of a knife.

Nev - er let you go, nev - er let me down.

Don't you give up,_____ na,__ na, na. I won't give up,___

mf

____ na,____ na, na. Let me love you, let me

love you. Don't you give up,___

___ na,_____ na, na. I won't give up,__

___ na,_____ na, na. Let me

love you, let me love you.

Not In Love

Words & Music by Fred Gibson, Edvard Erfjord, Henrik Michelsen, Rachel Keen & James Bell

The all-girl trio M.O formed back in 2012 and generated public interest later that year when they performed a remixed cover of Brandy & Monica's 'The Boy Is Mine' with rapper Lady Leshurr. Since then, they've become known for their 1990s throwback style in both fashion and music, leaving fans hoping for a debut album release in the near future.

Hints & Tips: This song has a Calypso rhythm. You can create this feel by playing dampened strings for the 'x' notes in the strumming pattern.

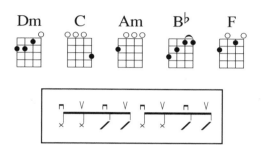

You're al - ways drunk when you come a - round,___

I know you think that you got me down.____

Fun - ny 'cause you could - n't be more wrong. I fought you

No Lie

**Words & Music by Sean Henriques, Jamie Sanderson, Philip Kembo,
Emily Schwartz & Andrew Jackson**

Sean Paul brought dancehall to the masses in 2002 with 'Gimme The Light', the first single from his debut album, *Dutty Rock*. Since then, he has continued to dominate the urban charts with hit after hit. He wrote 'No Lie' with two songwriters, one of whom was a friend of the singer Dua Lipa. The song was played to her and she loved it, so plans were made for Lipa to sing on the track with Sean Paul.

Hints & Tips: This song features an off-beat strumming pattern (see below). Practise slowly at first to get the up-strokes in the right place.

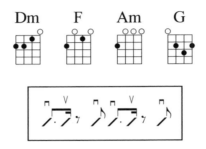

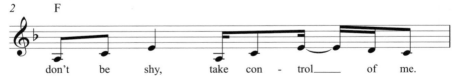

Jaunty ♩ = 96

Dm
Feel your eyes, they all o - ver me,
mf

2 F
don't be shy, take con - trol___ of me.

3 Am   G
Get the vibe, it's gon-na be lit to - night._ No lie.___

Now And Later

Words & Music by Ian Kirkpatrick, Andreas Schuller, Joe Spargur, Dominic Woods, James Wong & Leroy Clampitt

'Now And Later', from Sage The Gemini's album, *Bachelor Party*, was named after the American sweet of the same name. Now and Laters come in 19 flavours, but in the song, Sage The Gemini implies there are '31 flavours', believed to be a nod to his notion to write music that can 'please everybody' and access as many listeners as possible. In an interview, the artist revealed that he lost a wobbly tooth to one of the sweets when he was younger!

Hints & Tips: Try switching between strumming and playing the riff to create contrast between different sections.

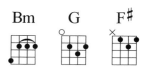

Bouncy ♩ = 104

I can be____ your life sa - ver,

treat me like____ a jaw - break - er.

You got thir - ty - one fla - vours,

ba - by, you can get this

now or la - ter, now or la -

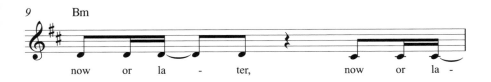

- ter. You can get this

now or la - ter, now or la -

D.C. al Fine
(*with repeats*)

- ter, your choice!

On Hold

**Words & Music by Daryl Hall, Sara Allen, John Oates,
James Smith, Romy Madley Croft & Oliver Sim**

Five years since their previous album, *Coexist*, The xx released *I See You* in 2017, with 'On Hold' as their
first single. The band is known for their understated, electropop style, which is evident in this track,
along with their distinctive alternate male and female vocal lines. However, the *I See You* album shows
The xx taking their style in a more playful direction, saying that the five-year hiatus was hugely beneficial
for their musical growth.

**Hints & Tips: Try varying the strumming pattern to be more open-sounding in the verse,
then tighten it up for the chorus.**

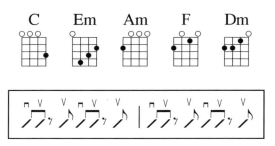

Wistful ♩ = 124

Rockabye

Words & Music by Steve McCutcheon, Sean Henriques, Ina Wroldsen, Ammar Malik & Jack Patterson

After their storming 2014 No. 1 hit, 'Rather Be', Clean Bandit released 'Rockabye' two years later to similarly raving reviews and another No. 1 spot. It was the first song released by the band after the departure of violinist Neil Milan, who was responsible for co-creating the group. The track features dancehall superstar Sean Paul and contemporary English singer-songwriter Anne-Marie.

Hints & Tips: This song features an off-beat strumming pattern (see below). Practise slowly at first to get the up-strokes in the right place.

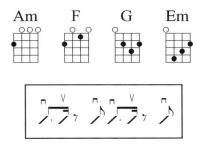

for her ba - by,   all on her own,_

no one will come, she's got to save_ him.   She tells him,

'oh,   love,_____ no____ one's ev - er gon - na hurt

you,   love,__ I'm__ gon - na give you all of

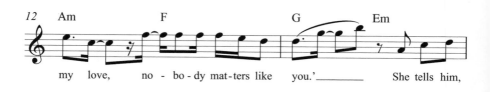

my love,   no - bo - dy mat-ters like you.'_____ She tells him,

'your life____ ain't__ gon' be noth - ing like

my life,___ you're___ going to grow and have a

good life,_ I'm_ gon-na do what I got to___ do.'___ So,

rock-a-bye,_ ba - by, rock-a-bye,___ I'm_ gon-na rock you.

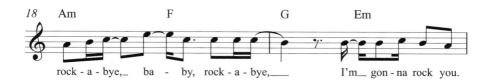

Rock-a-bye,_ ba - by, don't you cry,___ some-bo-dy's got you.

Rock-a-bye,_ ba - by, rock-a-bye,___ I'm_ gon-na rock you.

Rock-a-bye,_ ba - by, don't you cry,___ rock-a-bye,___

September Song

Words & Music by Benjamin McIldowie, Teemu Brunila, Jon Hume & John Paul Cooper

The Manchester-born singer-songwriter JP Cooper had been making waves in the underground music scene for a few years before he reached No. 1 in the UK Official Singles Chart when he appeared on Jonas Blue's track 'Perfect Strangers' in 2016. He was still relatively new to chart success when 'September Song' was released. The song describes a guy's feelings about a girl with whom he had a short-lived teenage romance.

Hints & Tips: This song uses the Bb chord which can be tricky for beginners. The 1st finger lays over two strings, make sure you keep the second and third fingers upright.

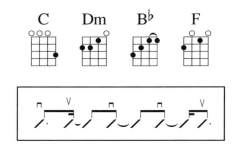

With a summery feel ♩ = 96

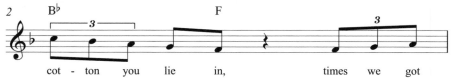

Our love was strong as a li - on, soft as the

mp

cot - ton you lie in, times we got

hot like an i - ron, you and I.

So Good

Words & Music by Steve Mac, Edward Drewett & Chelcee Grimes

This is the debut single from X Factor winner Louisa Johnson, who took the 12th UK series by storm back in 2015 and became the programme's youngest winner to date. Before releasing 'So Good', Johnson had already warmed up the crowd by working with electronic pop band Clean Bandit on their track, 'Tears', in 2016.

Hints & Tips: This song is played with a shuffle—a swing feel in the 16th notes (semiquavers). Listen to the original to make sure you have the right feel.

I said I'm 'bout five min - utes a - way,_ one more stop and I'll be off this train._ I'm free a - ny day of the week, al - ways

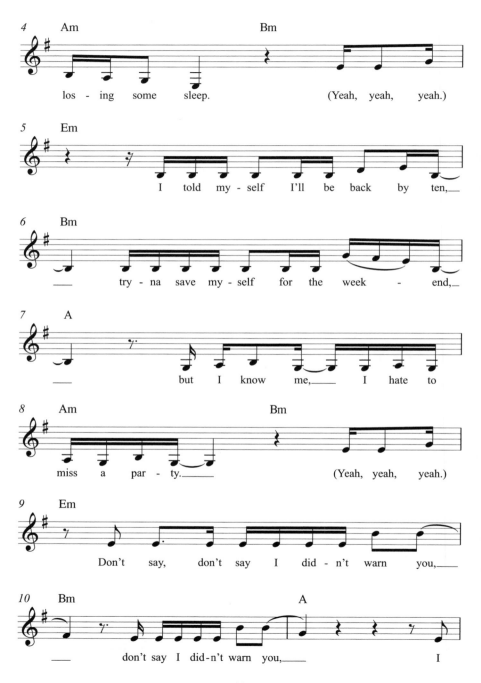

Shape Of You

Words & Music by Steve Mac, Ed Sheeran & John McDaid

Ed Sheeran co-wrote this track with Snow Patrol's Johnny McDaid and producer Steve Mac, and it appears on his 2017 album, ÷. Originally, Sheeran had intended to write the song for pop star Rihanna, but eventually chose to record it himself after deciding the lyrics weren't quite right for the other singer. Sheeran released this and 'Castle On The Hill' (page 10) simultaneously, scoring him both the No. 1 and No. 2 spots in the charts in record-breaking fashion!

Hints & Tips: Keep your strumming light and crisp to emulate the bouncy feel on the original track.

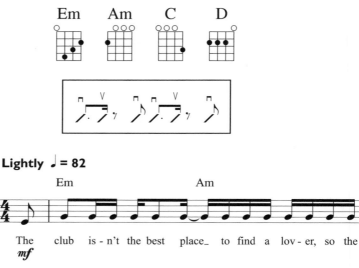

The club is-n't the best place to find a lov-er, so the

bar is where I go.

Me and my friends at the ta-ble, do-ing shots, drink-ing

Starboy

**Words & Music by Thomas Bangalter, Guy-Manuel de Homem-Christo,
Henry Russell Walter, Jason Quenneville, Abel Tesfaye & Martin McKinney**

This track's title was inspired by David Bowie's 'Starman', but this is where the similarities between the two
songs end. While Bowie focuses on the other-worldliness of a potential 'Starman', it is believed that 'Starboy'
is an introduction to The Weeknd's new alter ego, having chopped off his famous dreadlocks and used the
song's music video to debut his new look. The tune is the title track of his 2016 album of the same name.

Hints & Tips: When playing a fast strum like this, it is important to keep time between the chord changes.
It is fine to play open strings on the last couple of strums while you change chords.

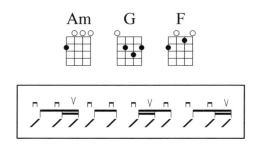

Precisely ♩ = 82

mp

I'm tryin' to   put   you   in   the   worst   mood,

ah.____   P - One   clean - er   than   your church   shoes,

ah.____   Mil - li   point   two,   just   to   hurt   you,

All red Lamb' just to tease you,

None of these toys on lease too,

Made your whole year in a week

too, ah. Main **** out of your league too,

ah. Side **** out of your league too,

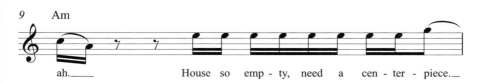

ah. House so emp - ty, need a cen - ter - piece.

10 G

_____ Twen - ty racks, a ta - ble carved from e - bo - ny.____

11 F

_____ Cut that i - v'ry in - to skin - ny piec -

12 G

- es, then she clean it with her face, man, I love my ba -

13 Am

- by. You talk - in' mon - ey, need a hear - in' aid.____

14 G

_____ You talk - in' 'bout me, I don't see the shade.__

15 F

_____ Switch up my style, I'll take a - ny lane.____

54

I'll   switch up   my   cup   if   I   kill   a - ny   pain.

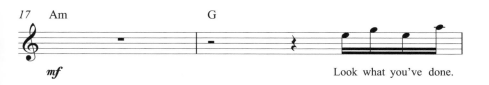

mf

Look what you've done.

I'm   a   mo' - **** - in'

star   -   boy._____

Look   what   you've   done.

I'm   a   mo' - **** - in'   star - boy._

We Don't Talk Anymore

Words & Music by Jacob Hindlin, Charlie Puth & Selena Gomez

Charlie Puth wrote this song after chatting to a friend who had been infatuated with a girl for months previously, but in a follow-up conversation, had said to him, 'we don't talk anymore'. In an attempt to lighten the mood, Puth started singing the phrase back to him, which resulted in the conception of the song. Selena Gomez agreed to feature on this track as she had experienced an on-off relationship in the public eye and felt she had a personal connection with the lyrics.

Hints & Tips: Clap through the rhythm of the strumming pattern a few times before you play—the semiquavers on beat 3 could catch you out! Remember, you can play the Bm* chord shape if you find the Bm shape tricky.

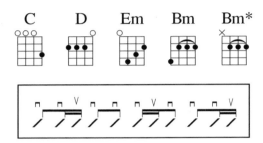

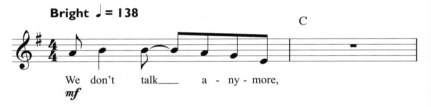

You Want Me

Words & Music by Luke Reid, Corey Johnson, Thomas Courtney & Darren Martyn

Tom Zanetti released this dance-house track, which became his first single to reach the charts, with Sadia Ama, the little sister of 'You Might Need Somebody' singer, Shola Ama. The Leeds-born entrepreneur describes himself as a 'man of all trades'—together with his music career as a DJ, producer, rapper and songwriter, Zanetti also clocks in ownership of four festivals as well as several overseas businesses and is looking to set up a barbershop and a clothing brand in the near future!

Hints & Tips: This song has no chords at all: just play the simple riff throughout.

Mysterious ♩ = 124

N.C.

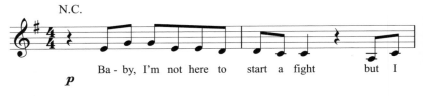

p

Ba - by, I'm not here to   start   a   fight   but   I

just   thought   I'd   let   you   know.

'Cause the way that you've been   treat - ing   me,   is   so   un -

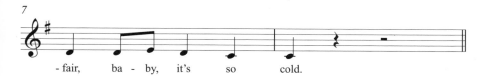

- fair, ba - by, it's so cold.

You want me, you want me,

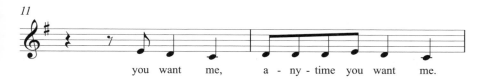

you want me, a - ny - time you want me.

You want me, you want me, you want me,

a - ny - time you want me too.

You Don't Know Me

**Words & Music by Uzoechi Emenike, Timucin Aluo, Janee Bennett, Rachel Keen,
Phil D Young, Peter Hayo, Walter Merziger, Arno Kammermeier & DJ Pat Bo**

For Jax Jones, settling on the perfect bass line was the most difficult part of writing 'You Don't Know Me'. Having been obsessed with M.A.N.D.Y vs Booka Shade's 2005 track, 'Body Language', for so long, he decided to try out their bassline with his own song and realised it was a match! Jones said that the combination was a perfect way of bringing 'classic techno to our new house setting'.

Hints & Tips: When playing a fast strum like this, it is important to keep time between the chord changes. It is fine to play open strings on the last couple of strums while you change chords.

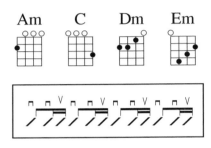

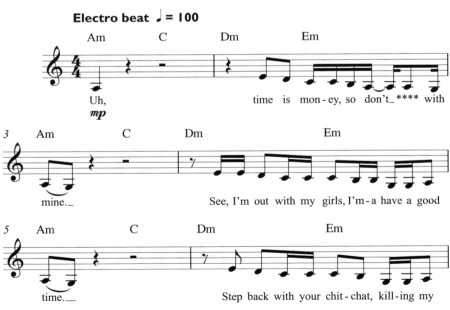

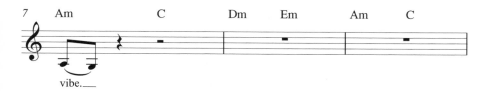

vibe.____

See, I can't get too much of a good thing.

S'why me - a dress up in the fi - nest things?_

Please hold your tongue, don't say a damn thing.

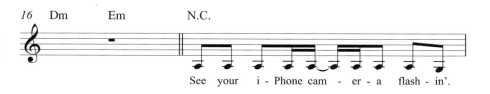

See your i - Phone cam - er - a flash - in'.

Please step back, it's my____ style you're cramp - in'.

19 You here for long? 'Oh, no,____ I'm just pass - in'.'

20 Do you want a drink? 'No,____ thanks for ask - in'.'

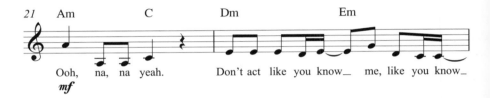

21 Am · C · Dm · Em

Ooh, na, na yeah. Don't act like you know__ me, like you know__

mf

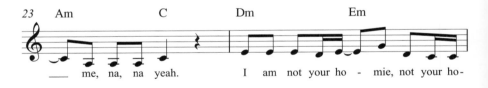

23 Am · C · Dm · Em

____ me, na, na yeah. I am not your ho - mie, not your ho-

25 Am · C · Dm · Em

- mie, na, na yeah. Don't act like you know__ me, like you know__

27 Am · C · Dm · Em

____ me, na, na yeah. You don't know me, **** yeah.

123456789